COLLINS•LONGMAN

Mapstart

MAPSTART 3 COPYMASTERS

In developing children's understanding of and skills in using maps it is essential that they explore and examine maps not only through reading and studying but also by recording on, adding to, completing and creating maps.

The **Mapstart Copymasters** have been prepared to provide opportunities for children to make marks on maps to foster their growing map ability.
The **copymasters** have been developed as a vital extension to the **Mapstart core books**. They provide further activities to reinforce ideas and skills introduced in the **core books** and introduce new ideas and skills to the children. The **copymasters** both refer to the maps and photographs in the **core books** and provide new material for the children to work on.

Each **copymaster** is linked to a section in the **core books**. The *page number(s)* at the bottom of the **copymasters** indicate the parallel pages in the **core book** to which each **copymaster** relates. The *Teacher's Notes* on the following 6 pages also give details of this information as well as outlining the focus of each **copymaster** and the National Curriculum aspects that are covered. Links are given between each **copymaster** and the statements of attainment being worked towards. Ideas for further activities are also included.

First published 1993, reprinted 1995, 1996, 1997, 1998, 1999, 2000 (twice), 2001, 2002
This edition © 1993 Collins-Longman Atlases
HarperCollins Publishers, Westerhill Rd, Bishopbriggs, Glasgow G64 2QT
ISBN 0 00 360 320 2
Pearson Education Limited, Edinburgh Gate, Harlow, Essex CM20 2JE
ISBN 0 582 20939 0
Printed in the U.K.

Acknowledgement
Map for Copymaster No.7 was based on a Goad shopping centre plan with the permission of Chas. E. Goad Ltd., Salisbury Square, Old Hatfield, Hertfordshire, AL9 5BJ.

PL11362

Teacher's Notes

CORE BOOK	COPYMASTER	FOCUS
pp 2-3 Mapping the locality	1 LOOKING AT PLANS	• matching plans to oblique views • finding correct plan shapes on a map • colour coding and use of a key • link to photo **A** and map **H**
p 4 Grid references	2 GRID REFERENCES	• reinforcing use of four-figure grid references • link to map **A** on page 4
p 5 Compass directions	3 COMPASS DIRECTIONS	• reinforcing use of compass directions • eight points of the compass • use of four-figure grid reference • link to map **C** on page 5
pp 6-7 Measuring on the map	4 PLAN AND MAP	• measuring the length of objects, reinforcing use of the scale bar • comparing lengths of objects, using different scales • making a map, putting features in order, using symbols, grid references, compass directions and scale
	5 MEASURING ON THE MAP	• use of a scale bar • measuring straight line distances • follows on from Copymaster 4
	6 KNOWING ABOUT THE MAP	• the margin information around a map • reinforcing understanding of: title, symbols and key, grid references, compass, scale bar • locating and drawing the plan of an additional feature • follows on from Copymaster 5
pp 8-9 Using maps in a local survey	7 COLOUR CODING THE MAP	• using survey information to colour code a map • use of a key to colour code services
pp 10-11 Using maps as records and plans	8 BLACKBURN OLD AND NEW	• change in a locality • using maps to identify continuity and change • planning a new development • link to maps **A** and **D**
pp 12-13 Using maps to plan a journey	9 A JOURNEY IN TOWN	• following journey routes on maps • planning routes using maps
	10 USING THE METRO	• identifying features on maps • following routes on maps • follows on from Copymaster 9
pp 14-15 Landshape - hills on maps	11 LAND SHAPE	• identify features on the picture map • introduction to relief features on maps • matching correct views and maps of an area • links to **A** on page 14
	12 IN THE YORKSHIRE DALES	• transferring information from picture map to a road map • using symbols and key • locating features and slope on a map • link to **A** on page 14 • follows on from Copymaster 11
p 16 Landshape - showing height on maps	13 LOOKING AT SLOPES	• using photo and map to identify slope • link to **A** and **B** on page 16 • selecting correct cross-section for map • follows on from Copymaster 12
	14 HIGHER AND LOWER	• different steepnesses of slopes: gentle, steep, vertical • link to **B** on page 16 • making a relief map using symbols • follows on from Copymaster 13

FURTHER IDEAS	NATIONAL CURRICULUM GEOGRAPHY POS LINKS
• children to match plans to photos of local features • finding correct plans from distractors on local area map • children to make their own key for local area map	• interpreting symbols on a map • making a key **KS2 / 3d** *plans*
• children can make their own grid words, eg using their own initials, for others to work out from grid references • using local area or other locality maps, practice finding features using grid references	• use of four-figure grid references to locate features on a map **KS2 / 3d** *4-figure grid references*
• using local area street maps, follow compass directions • children to provide instructions for friends to follow, using compass directions	• use of the eight points of the compass **KS2 / 3d** *compass directions* *grid references*
• measure and draw scale plans of objects in the classroom • use the map as the basis for a story • children to create their own instructions for a map of an imaginary place	• measure straight line distances • use of compass points and grid references **KS2 / 3c** *make map* **KS2 / 3d** *plans*
• use scale bar to measure distances on local area map	• measuring straight line distances between features on a map, using scale **KS2 / 3d** *measure distance*
• measure distances on the map • practice giving/finding grid references • give instructions for routes around the flat using compass directions, related to specific activities • children to create their own maps of floors or open spaces	• use of four-figure grid references, compass points and symbols with key • measure straight line distances **KS2 / 3d** *plan* *measure distance*
• undertake a similar exercise using a different Goad shopping centre plan • survey shops/buildings/land-use in local area • make a colour coded map based on classification of services/functions/land-use	• using maps to find out where features are and where activities take place • investigate use of land and buildings • types of services **KS2 / 2c** *analyse evidence* **KS2 / 3d** *use maps*
• compare old and current maps of the local area • map continuity and change on a current local area map	• interpreting symbols on maps • looking at change in a locality **KS2 / 3d** *use maps* **KS2 / 5d** *change*
• use maps of local area to follow/plan routes • collect maps of other area, eg town/city centre, leisure centre, and plan routes	• follow routes using maps • use of compass directions • measuring distances using scale **KS2 / 3d** *routes*
• collect a variety of maps to use in planning routes, eg street/road, bus/coach, rail/underground maps • compare maps for their purpose, content, clarity, usefulness • involve children in planning routes on journeys made from school for fieldtrips and other visits	• follow routes using maps **KS2 / 3d** *routes*
• identify other features on **A** on page 14 • identify features on oblique photos of areas • show photos of hilly and mountainous areas	• interpreting relief maps **KS2 / 3d** *maps* **KS3 / 3d** *relief and landscape features*
• undertake a similar exercise using road maps and oblique views	• interpreting relief maps **KS2 / 3d** *maps* **KS3 / 3d** *relief and landscape features*
• use similar maps and cross-sections based on the local area or another locality • children to make their own arrow maps and cross-sections	• interpreting relief maps **KS2 / 3d** *plans* **KS3 / 3d** *cross-sections*
• children to make their own maps showing relief features • reinforce understanding that water flows downhill	• interpreting relief maps • using symbols to show information **KS2 / 3d** *maps* **KS3 / 3d** *cross-sections* *relief and landscape features*

Teacher's Notes

CORE BOOK	COPYMASTER	FOCUS
p17 Landshape - contours	15 SPOT HEIGHTS AND CONTOURS	• reinforcing idea of spot heights showing height of land • using spot heights to make a contour map • link to **C** on page 17
	16 CONTOURS	• relating shape and slope to contour patterns • follows on from Copymaster 15
	17 CONTOURS AND SLOPES	• interpreting information about slope and height from contour lines • links to **C** on page 17 • follows on from Copymaster 16
pp 18-19 Decreasing scales - a local area	18 SIX-FIGURE GRID REFERENCES	• reinforcing use of six-figure grid references • making a map using grid reference, contour, compass direction and scale information
	19 THE MAP PUZZLE	• reinforcing the idea of a map grid • matching correct map segments to the map • link to **A** on page 18
	20 SHAPES AND PATTERNS ON THE MAP 1	• adding information to a base map from another map • link to **C** on page 19
pp 20-21 Decreasing scales - towns and regions	21 SHAPES AND PATTERNS ON THE MAP 2	• adding information to a base map from another map • link to **A** on page 20
	22 SHAPES AND PATTERNS ON THE MAP 3	• adding information to a base map from another map • identifying grid squares on a map • matching a pattern to a map • link to **B** on page 21
pp 22-23 The shape of the Earth	23 VIEWS OF THE GLOBE	• introducing the term 'hemisphere' • reinforcement of names of continents and oceans
	24 FROM GLOBE TO MAP	• reinforcement of hemisphere view • relating hemisphere views to world map • idea that areas on a globe can be drawn on a map • follows on from Copymaster 23
pp 24-25 Where on Earth are we? Latitude and longitude	25 LATITUDE AND LONGITUDE 1	• reinforcing idea of latitude and longitude • identifying lines of latitude and longitude • links to **A**, **B** and **D** on page 24
	26 LATITUDE AND LONGITUDE 2	• locating places using latitude and longitude • link to map **E** on page 25 • link to world map on pages 44-45 • follows on from Copymaster 25
	27 LATITUDE AND LONGITUDE 3	• finding places using latitude and longitude • follows on from Copymaster 26

FURTHER IDEAS	NATIONAL CURRICULUM GEOGRAPHY POS LINKS
• provide children with similar spot height maps, based on the local area or another locality • children to make their own spot height maps for others to complete	• interpreting relief maps **KS3 / 3d** *relief and landscape features*
• create similar activities based on local area or another locality • discuss what is looked for in the contour pattern to relate it correctly to the shape and slope of the land	• interpreting relief maps **KS3 / 3d** *relief and landscape features*
• undertake similar activities on contour maps of the local area or another locality • use 1:10 000 scale Ordnance Survey maps to identify slope, height and shape of land using contours	• interpreting relief maps **KS3 / 3d** *relief and landscape features*
• children to make their own six-figure grid patterns for others to complete • children to make their own maps using symbols, grid references, compass directions, scale and height information	• use six-figure grid references to locate features on a map **KS2 / 3d** *grid references* **KS3 / 3d** *6-figure grid references*
• create a similar exercise using the local area 1:10 000 or 1:25 000 scale Ordnance Survey map • use the map for marking routes for journeys, using arrows to show direction of slope, colouring land above/below certain heights, finding features at six-figure grid references, measuring distances	• interpreting symbols on maps • use of 1:25 000 scale map **KS2 / 3d** *grid references* **KS3 / 3d** *relief and landscape features*
• children to add information to an incomplete base map of the local area or another locality • provide an outline map of part of your local 1:50 000 scale Ordnance Survey map to undertake similar exercises	• use of 1:50 000 scale Ordnance Survey map **KS2 / 1c** *map patterns* **KS2 / 3d** *maps* **KS3 / 3d** *map features*
• undertake similar exercises on road maps covering your local area	• interpreting symbols using a key **KS2 / 1c** *map patterns* **KS3 / 3d** *map patterns*
• create similar exercises using road maps for the local area	• using symbols and a key • using four-figure grid references • extracting information from a distribution pattern on a map **KS2 / 1c** and **KS3 / 3d** *map patterns*
• use a globe to look at different views of the Earth as it rotates • find out about the Earth's rotation, how and why it moves on its axis and around the sun • provide other hemisphere views for the children to identify, including views from the poles	• continents named on maps C and F in the Geography Programmes of Study **KS2 / 3d** *globe* *maps C(E), 4(W)*
• collect photos of the Earth from space • use an inflatable, transparent globe to see features opposite each other on the Earth's surface • cut up an old hollow ball or an inflatable globe to lay it flat to show the problem in making a map of a sphere	• recognising that a globe can be represented as a flat surface **KS2 / 3d** *globe, map* *maps C(E), 4(W)*
• on a globe identify the lines of latitude and longitude • find lines of latitude and longitude on atlas maps • create a giant world map with lines of latitude and longitude superimposed	• using latitude and longitude to locate places on atlas maps **KS3 / 3d** *grid references* *maps F(E), 8(W)*
• using a suitable atlas, give other places to find from their latitude/longitude grid reference	• using latitude and longitude to locate places on atlas maps **KS3 / 3d** *grid references* *maps F(E), 8(W)*
• using a suitable atlas, give other places to find from their latitude/longitude grid reference • children to set similar exercises for their friends	• using latitude and longitude to find places on atlas maps **KS3 / 3d** *grid references* *maps F(E), 8(W)*

Teacher's Notes

CORE BOOK	COPYMASTER	FOCUS
pp 26-27 Introducing atlas maps	28 WHAT DOES THE MAP SHOW?	• reinforcing awareness of the information around the margin of a map • follows on from Copymaster 6 • links to pages 20-21
pp 28-29 U.K. - Scotland and Northern Ireland	29 SHAPES AND PATTERNS IN BRITAIN 1	• developing idea of patterns shown on the map • link to map **A** on pages 28-29 • follows on from Copymaster 22
pp 30-31 U.K. - England and Wales	30 SHAPES AND PATTERNS IN BRITAIN 2	• developing awareness of distribution patterns • reinforcing use of latitude and longitude • links to map **A** on pages 30-31 • follows on from Copymaster 29
pp 32-33 British Isles - Recreation	31 HOLIDAY JOURNEYS	• planning routes for journeys • use of a thematic map, showing major roads • follows on from Copymasters 9 and 10 • relate to Recreation map on page 32
pp 34-35 British Isles - Population	32 LOOKING AT THEMATIC MAPS	• looking for distribution patterns on maps • links to maps **A** and **C** on pages 32-33 and map **A** on page 34
pp 36-37 Weather maps	33 MAP THE WEATHER	• making a weather map from a forecast • use of weather symbols
pp 38-39 British Isles	34 THE BRITISH ISLES	• reinforcing recall of shape of British Isles • completing a grid pattern using latitude/longitude • identifying features using an atlas map • links to map **B** on page 39
pp 40-41 Europe	35 EUROPE	• reinforcing recall of the shape of Europe • identifying features using an atlas map • links to photo **A** and map **B** on pages 40-41
	36 SHAPES AND PATTERNS IN EUROPE	• reinforcing identification of countries from their shapes • looking at distribution patterns on maps • identifying features using an atlas map • links to photo **A** and map **B** on pages 40-41
pp 42-43 The World - Countries	37 WORLD MAP - COUNTRIES	• knowledge of countries of the world • link to map **A** on pages 42-43
pp 44-45 The World - Physical features	38 WORLD MAP - PHYSICAL FEATURES	• knowledge of physical features of the world • link to map **A** on pages 44-45
	39 WORLD MAP	• map of the world on which to mark features and places as a record • link to maps on pages 42-43 and 44-45
pp 46-47 United Kingdom index/World index	40 MAKING AN INDEX	• using and making an index for an atlas map • use of latitude and longitude • link to map **A** on page 32

FURTHER IDEAS	NATIONAL CURRICULUM LINKS
• select another map for which to undertake a similar exercise • remind children to include margin information on their own maps as appropriate	• use of four-figure grid references, compass points and symbols with key • measure straight line distances **KS2 / 3d** *maps and symbols*
• look for land-use patterns in other grid squares • practice giving/finding latitude/longitude grid references	• distribution patterns shown on maps **KS2 / 1c** *map patterns*
• practice reading latitude/longitude grid references • identify other land-use patterns on the map	• distribution patterns shown on maps **KS2 / 1c** *map patterns*
• ask the children to draw return journeys via different routes • find the places visited on the journey on the Recreation map on page 32 • find the routes on a national road atlas/map	• using information from a distribution pattern shown on a thematic map • finding/following routes on a map **KS2 / 3d** *routes* *maps A(E), 2(W)*
• children to make British Isles maps which show distribution patterns from the Recreation or Population maps	• identify distribution patterns on atlas maps **KS2 / 3d** *maps* **KS3 / 3e** *information on atlas maps*
• collect written forecasts from the daily press and map the forecast information • collect daily weather maps in the press • on British Isles/Europe maps locate the resorts listed in **E** on page 37	• making a map showing a distribution pattern **KS2 / 3c** *make map* **KS3 / 3f** *graphic techniques on maps*
• use the map to record places of interest and places encountered in their work by the children, eg places in the news or patterns being studied, such as transport networks	• maps A and D in the Geography Programmes of Study **KS2 / 3d** *maps A(E), 2(W)* **KS3 / 3d** *maps D(E), 5(W)*
• use the map to record places of interest and places encountered in their work by the children, eg places in the news or countries in the European Community	• maps B and E in the Geography Programmes of Study **KS2 / 3d** *maps B(E), 3(W)* **KS3 / 3d** *maps E(E), 7(W)*
• children could develop similar exercises of their own for maps of other continents • whenever children encounter a place find it on a globe or suitable atlas map • discuss location of countries eg landlocked, sea access, number of shared borders	• maps B and E in the Geography Programmes of Study **KS2 / 3d** *maps B(E), 3(W)* **KS2 / 3d** *maps E(E), 7(W)*
• periodically look through several newspapers/TV news reports and record the countries mentioned to see which come up frequently • compare relative sizes of countries and relate to size of British Isles • find out which continent has most countries	• maps C and F in the Geography Programmes of Study **KS2 / 3d** *maps C(E), 4(W)* **KS3 / 3d** *maps F(E), 8(W)*
• record physical features which are mentioned in news reports, eg oceans/seas, islands, rivers • look at distribution pattern of specific features, eg mountain ranges, deserts • relate location of countries to physical features	• maps C and F in the Geography Programmes of Study **KS2 / 3d** *maps C(E), 4(W)* **KS3 / 3d** *maps F(E), 8(W)*
• use map to mark on specific distribution patterns, eg mountain ranges, capital cities	• maps C and F of the Geography Programmes of Study **KS2 / 3d** *maps C(E), 4(W)* **KS3 / 3d** *maps F(E), 8(W)*
• make an index for another map, eg England on pages 30-31 or the towns on the Population map on page 34 • make an index using six-figure grid references for one of the maps on pages 18-21	• finding information using the index **KS2 / 3d** *maps A(E), 1(W), 4(W), using index* **KS3 / 3d** *maps D(E), 5(W), 6(W)* **KS3 / 3e** *use atlas index*

1 Looking at plans

Name ....

1 Look at the plans next to each picture. Colour the plan that goes with the picture.

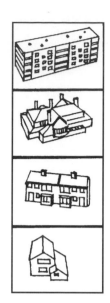 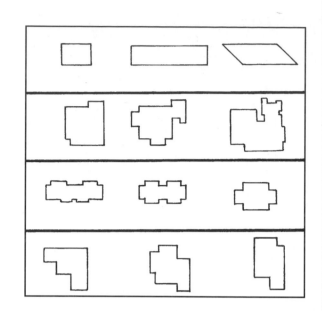

2 Look at the plans in the box. You can find six of these plans on map **H** on page 3. Colour the six correct plans.

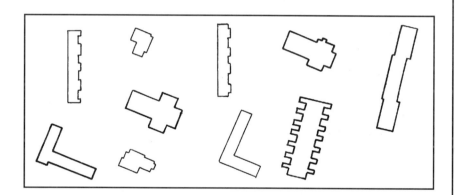

3 This is a map of Hillmead. It has been drawn smaller. Colour all the buildings yellow.

4 Make a key for the map.

KEY

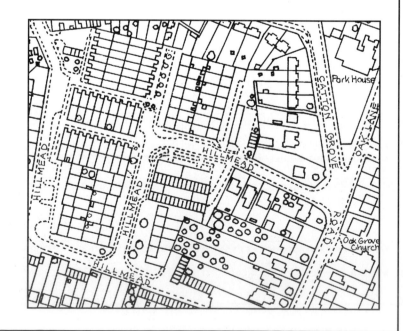

2 Grid References

Name ....

1 This word is in grid code.
To read the word colour these
grid squares:
10,40; 12,43; 16,40; 20,40; 10,41; 12,42;
16,41; 20,41; 18,44; 14,42; 18,43; 22,42;
14,40; 18,41; 11,44; 17,44; 22,43; 18,42;
14,41; 16,42; 20,44; 10,43; 14,44; 21,42;
17,42; 10,44; 20,43; 12,44; 22,44; 16,43;
10,42; 18,40; 13,44; 20,42; 16,44; 14,43;
21,44.

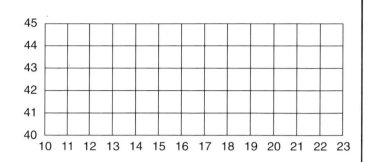

2 Spot the shape.
Find grid reference 72,13.
Mark a dot where the lines cross.
Now find 81,13. Mark it.
Join them with a line.
Now find 81,11. Join it to 81,13.
Join up these grid references in order
from 81,11:
86,11; 86,13; 88,13; 88,18; 86,18; 86,20;
83,20; 83,21; 82,21; 82,20; 81,20; 81,18;
72,18; 72,13.

3 Colour in brown the shape you have
drawn.
Find the shape on map A on page 4.
What is it? _____

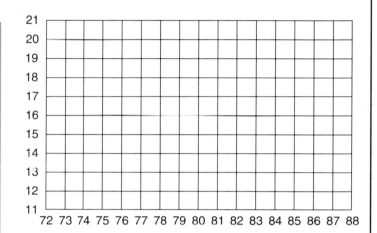

This is a map of Hillmead.
It shows the numbers of
the homes in Hillmead.

4 Write the
four-figure grid
references for these
homes:
33   __,__
120   __,__
94   __,__
1-15 __,__
22   __,__
74   __,__

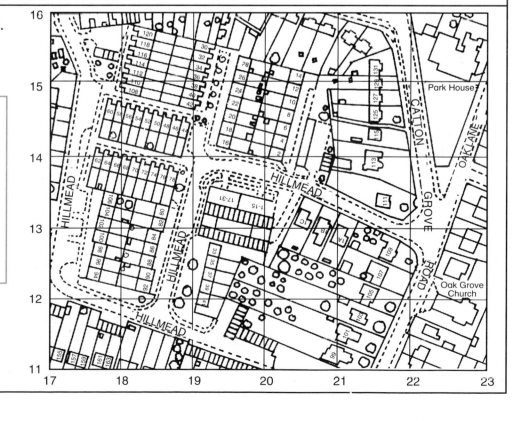

Page 4 Grid references

3 Compass Directions

Name ....

Follow the compass directions to find out where to go.
Each direction tells you which way to turn at the next turning.
Draw your routes on the street maps.

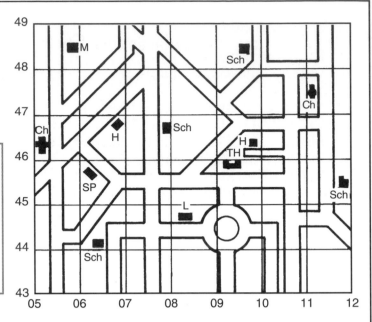

1 Start at the school in 06,44.
   Go: N, E, E, SE, NE, NW, N, E, N, W.
   Stop by the building on your right.
   Write your grid reference: __,__

2 Start at the north of the building in 11,47.
   Go: W, SW, NW, S, SW, SW, N, N.
   Stop at the building.
   Give your grid reference: __,__

KEY		P	Post Office	Sch	School
Ch	Church	TH	Town Hall	M	Mosque
SP	Swimming Pool	L	Library	H	Hall

This is a map of the area around Hillmead.

3 Start at the junction of Woodcock Road and St. Clements Hill. Go west. At the first junction turn south. At the first junction turn east. Name the road you are in:_____

4 Start at the school on St. Clements Hill. Go west along Chamberlin Road. At the end of the road turn north to the first set of shops. Turn west. Take the fourth road north. Stop by the building to your east. What is the building used for? _____

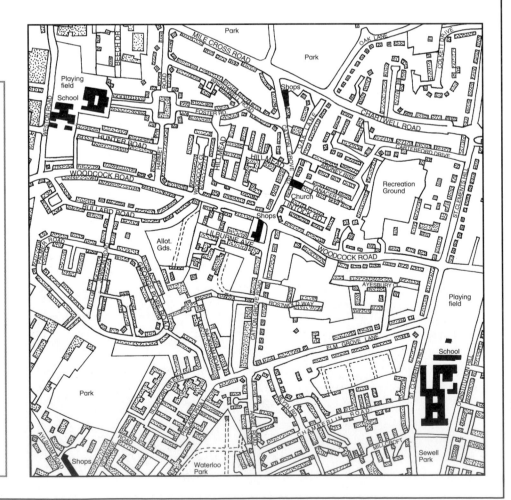

4 Plan and map

Name ....

Look at these plans.
Each object has been drawn smaller than its real size.
Below each one is a measuring bar.
Use it to help you work out the real size of each object.

1 In red, colour the longest real object.
2 In blue, colour the shortest real object.
3 In yellow, colour the object that is really 60 cm long.

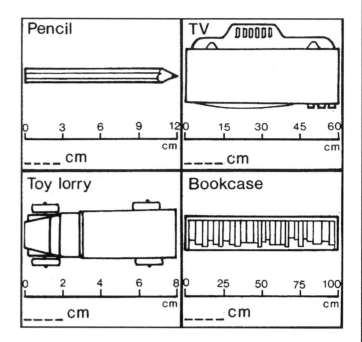

Pencil

```
0    3    6    9    12
                      cm
____ cm
```

TV

```
0    15   30   45   60
                      cm
____ cm
```

Toy lorry

```
0    2    4    6    8
                     cm
____ cm
```

Bookcase

```
0    25   50   75   100
                       cm
____ cm
```

4 Can you draw this map?
Read the message and draw the map it describes on the grid.
"Get off bus stop (50,38). Pass post box (52,39). Cross road to right, zebra crossing (53,38). Walk S, path (45m), circular pond (14m across). Walk quarter way right, go SW wooded path, centre (51,31). To left path hidden (trees and bushes), follow E to hut (56,31), fence round. Seek what is pinned inside the hut. Follow."

5 To complete the map draw what you think is in the rest of the area.

6 What might be pinned inside the hut?
Write a story to explain what happens.

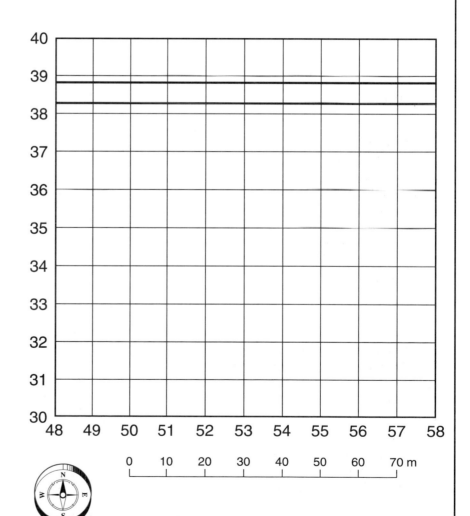

Pages 6-7 Measuring on the map

5 Measuring on the map   Name ....

This is a map of Hillmead.
Below the map is a scale bar.
On the map the roads are named.
Some buildings are named or have numbers
on them.

Use the scale bar to help you measure
straight line distances on the map.
Always measure from the centre of a building.

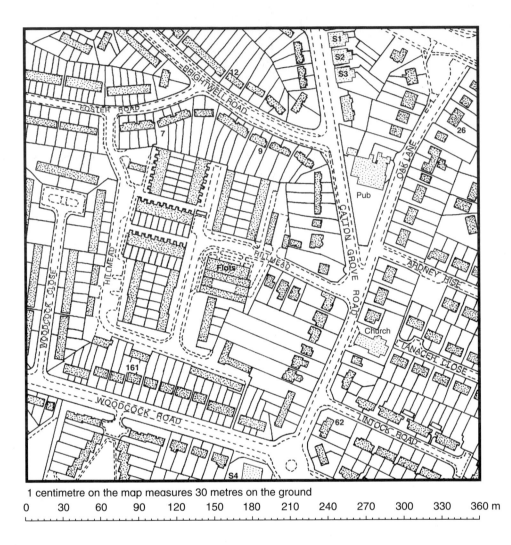

1 centimetre on the map measures 30 metres on the ground

0   30   60   90   120   150   180   210   240   270   300   330   360 m

1   How many metres is it from the flats to
    the church? _____m
2   How far is it from 9 Brightwell Road to
    shop S3? _____m
3   How far is it to the pub from
    161 Woodcock Road? _____m
4   How long is Lintock Road? _____m
5   How long is the block of flats? _____m
6   What is the distance from shop S1 to 62
    Catton Grove Road? _____m

7   How far is it from the
    roundabout to 7 Foster Road?
    _____m
8   How much longer is Woodcock Close
    than Lintock Road? _____m
9   How far is it from 12 Brightwell Road to
    26 Oak Lane? _____m
10 What is the distance from shop S4 to
    shop S2? _____m

6 Knowing about the map

Name ....

This is a plan of

_____

1 On this plan the title, key, compass, grid lines and scale bar have not been finished. Work them out and put them in the spaces round the plan.

These clues may help you:
*you come upstairs to sleep.
*in the largest room is a cupboard.
*the doors opposite each other are 2.5m apart.
*the stairs are west of the bathroom.
*the grid lines are 2cm apart; the first grid reference is 14,25.

2 On the plan draw a table 50cm long and 50cm wide under the northwest window of the room 4m long and 3m wide. What is its grid reference? ___,___

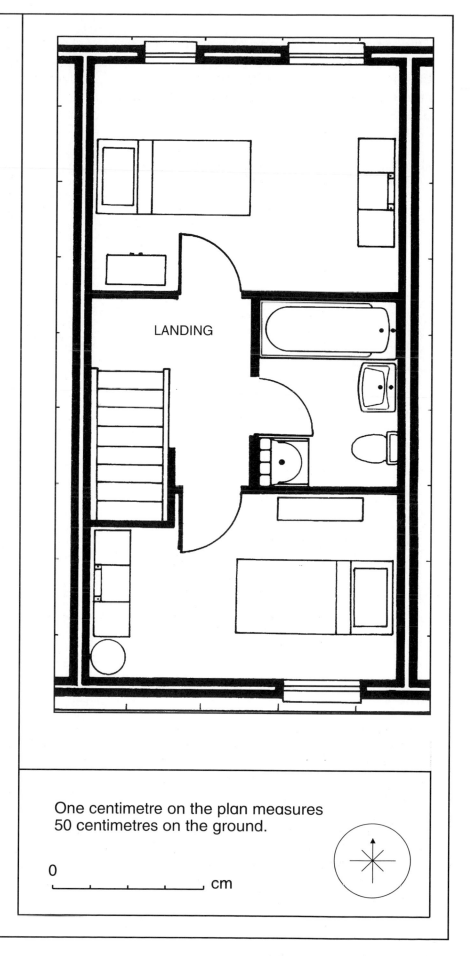

LANDING

KEY

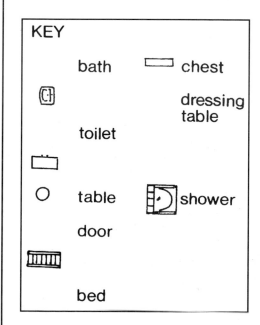

bath   chest

dressing table

toilet

table   shower

door

bed

One centimetre on the plan measures 50 centimetres on the ground.

0 _____ cm

7 Colour coding the map

Name ....

This is an annotated map of a shopping centre.
It shows the shops and the main types of item they sell.
It is part of a Goad Plan of Blackburn's shopping centre.

Use the information on the survey map to colour code the categories of services.

1 Choose a different colour for each category of service in the key.
Colour each box in the key.
2 Decide which category of service each shop offers.
Use your colours in the key to colour code each shop by its service.
3 Make a graph to show how many shops are in each category of service.

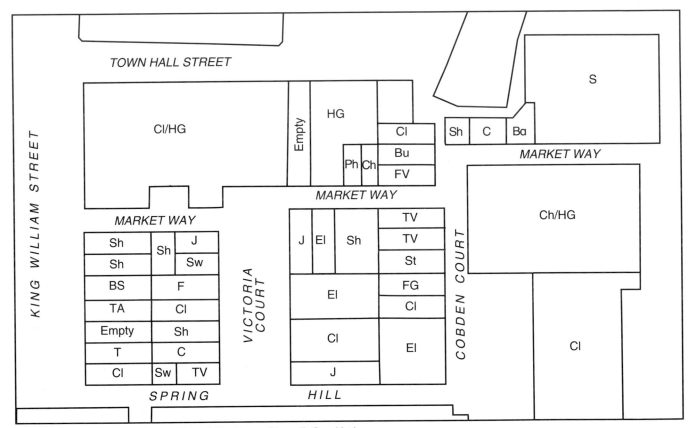

Based on Goad Shopping Centre Plan of Blackburn, Chas. E. Goad Ltd.

Abbreviations

Ba	Baker	HG	Household goods
BS	Building Society	J	Jeweller
Bu	Butcher	Ph	Photographic shop
C	Card shop	S	Supermarket
Ch	Chemist	Sh	Shoe shop
Cl	Clothes shop	St	Stationer
El	Electrical shop	Sw	Sweet shop
F	Food shop	T	Telephone shop
FG	Fancy goods	TA	Travel Agent
FV	Fruit and veg. shop	TV	Television rentals

KEY

☐ Food and drink

☐ Household goods and services

☐ Clothes and shoes

☐ Chemists

☐ Electrical goods and services

☐ Stationery

☐ Travel services

☐ Luxury goods

☐ Specialist services

☐ Empty

8   Blackburn old and new   Name ....

You will need to use pages 10 and 11 to help you.

This is a copy of map **A** of
Railway Road.
Compare this map with map **D**
on page 11 showing Railway
Road in 1893.

> **?**
>
> 1   Colour red the
>   buildings which
>   have been built since
>   1893.
> 2   Colour yellow the
>   buildings which have
>   survived since 1893.

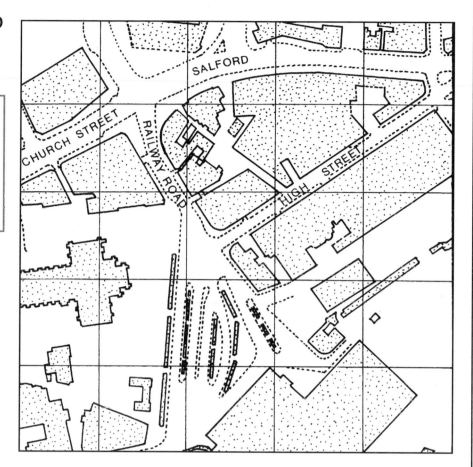

This is part of map **A** on page 10.
The area to the north and south of the
High Street is to be rebuilt.

> **?**
>
> 3   Decide what you would like
>   to build on the High Street site.
>   Draw your plans on the map and
>   complete the key.

KEY

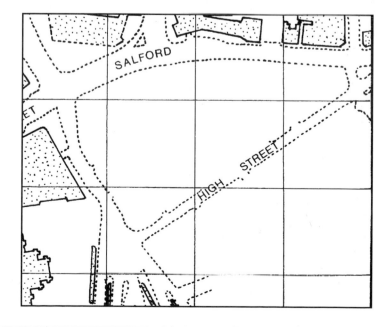

Pages 10-11 Using maps as records and plans

9 A journey into town

Name ....

This is a street map of central Newcastle.
Use it to follow and plan journeys.

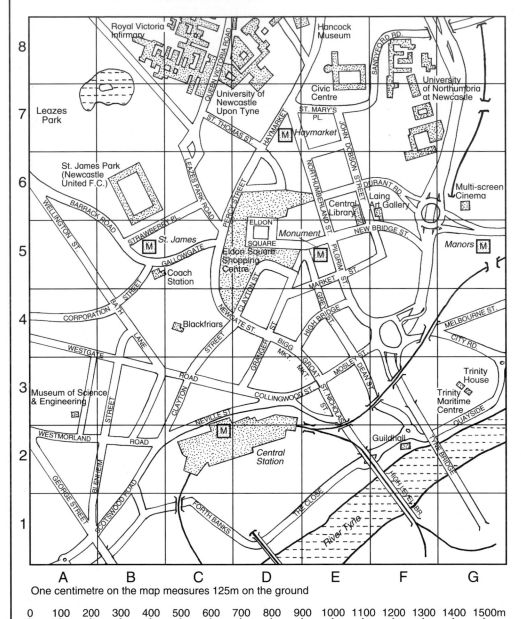

One centimetre on the map measures 125m on the ground

0 100 200 300 400 500 600 700 800 900 1000 1100 1200 1300 1400 1500m

KEY

	Important building
	Water
	Road
	Railway
	Bridge
M	Metro station

1 Draw this route on the map:
   You arrive at Central Station and come out into Neville Street.
   Turn east and follow the road northeast to the first large roundabout.
   Go northwest and take the third turning on the left.
   Name the place you come into:

   _____

   Name the grid square it is in: __,__
2 What is the straight line distance from Central Station to St. James Park? __,__m
3 On the map draw the shortest route from Central Station to St. James Park.
4 You arrive at Manors Metro Station to visit the cinema nearby, the Laing Art Gallery, the Hancock Museum, the Guildhall and the Museum of Science and Engineering. You finish at the coach station.
   Draw a route to show the best way to go.

Pages 12-13 Using maps to plan a journey

10 Using the metro

Name ....

Tina, Dick, Sue and Dipak have been to watch Newcastle United F.C. play at St. James Park. They leave to go home.

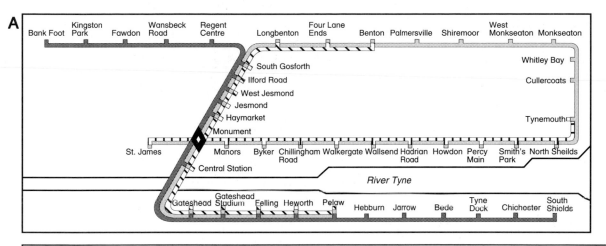

A

Bank Foot, Kingston Park, Fawdon, Wansbeck Road, Regent Centre, Longbenton, Four Lane Ends, Benton, Palmersville, Shiremoor, West Monkseaton, Monkseaton

Whitley Bay, Cullercoats, Tynemouth

South Gosforth, Ilford Road, West Jesmond, Jesmond, Haymarket, Monument

St. James, Manors, Byker, Chillingham Road, Walkergate, Wallsend, Hadrian Road, Howdon, Percy Main, Smith's Park, North Sheilds

Central Station

River Tyne

Gateshead, Gateshead Stadium, Felling, Heworth, Pelaw, Hebburn, Jarrow, Bede, Tyne Dock, Chichester, South Shields

KEY

▬▬▬ Metroline 1   ╱╱╱ Metroline 2   ▬▬▬ Metroline 3   ⊏⊐ Metroline 4   ◆ Monument interchange

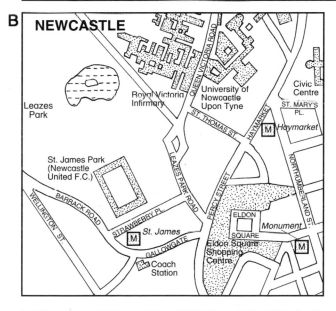

B NEWCASTLE

Leazes Park, Royal Victoria Infirmary, University of Newcastle Upon Tyne, Civic Centre, ST. MARY'S PL., Haymarket, St. James Park (Newcastle United F.C.), St. James, Eldon Square Shopping Centre, Coach Station, ELDON SQUARE, Monument, QUEEN VICTORIA ROAD, ST. THOMAS ST., HAYMARKET, LEAZES PARK ROAD, PERCY STREET, STRAWBERRY PL., GALLOWGATE, BARRACK ROAD, WELLINGTON ST., NORTHUMBERLAND ST.

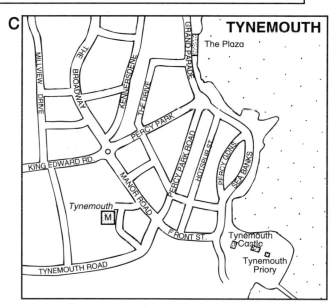

C TYNEMOUTH

The Plaza, MILLVIEW DRIVE, THE BROADWAY, GRAND PARADE, KENFERSDENE, THE DRIVE, PERCY PARK, KING EDWARD RD., MANOR ROAD, PERCY PARK ROAD, HOTSPUR ST., PERCY GDNS., SEA BANKS, Tynemouth, FRONT ST., TYNEMOUTH ROAD, Tynemouth Castle, Tynemouth Priory

KEY

░ Important building   ⌐ ¬ Pond   ⌐·¬ Sea   ▬ Road   Ⓜ Metro station

N W E S (compass)

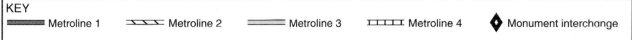

1 On maps **A** and **B** put an X on the nearest metro station to St. James Park they can use.
2 Tina goes home to Fawdon. On map **A** draw a green line to show her route on the metro.
3 Dick lives in Pelaw. On map **A** draw a red line to show his route on the metro.
4 Sue and Dipak go home to Tynemouth Metro Station. On map **A** draw a blue line to show their route.
5 From Tynemouth Metro Station Sue walks to meet friends at The Plaza. On map **C** draw her route.
6 Dipak walks home from the station to his home half way along the west side of Sea Banks. Draw his route.

11 Landshape

This is a sketch of the area of Buckden in **A** on page 14.

1 Use **A** to help you colour:
   the roads red
   the river blue
   the woods green
2 On the sketch draw arrows (→) to show which way the land slopes downhill.

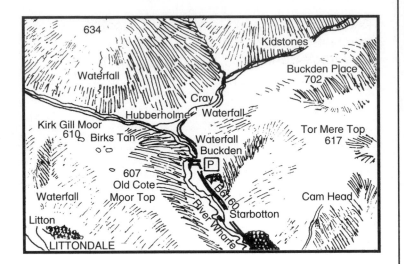

Look at the sketch on the left of a hilly landscape.
3 Which of the three maps shows the hilly landscape? Colour the correct map.

Sketch   **Maps**

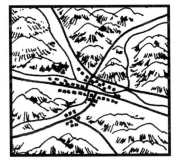   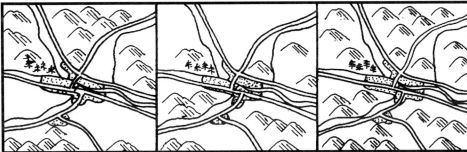

Look at the map on the left of a landscape.
4 Which of the three sketches shows the landscape in the map? Colour the correct sketch.

Map   **Sketches**

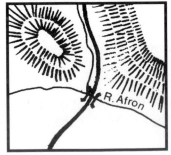   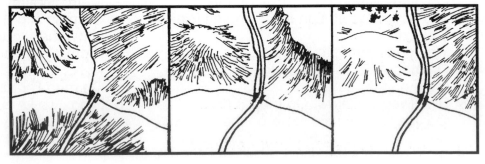

Pages 14-15 Landshape — hills on maps

12 In the Yorkshire Dales

Name ....

The road map shows the area in **A** on page 14.
Use **A** to help you.

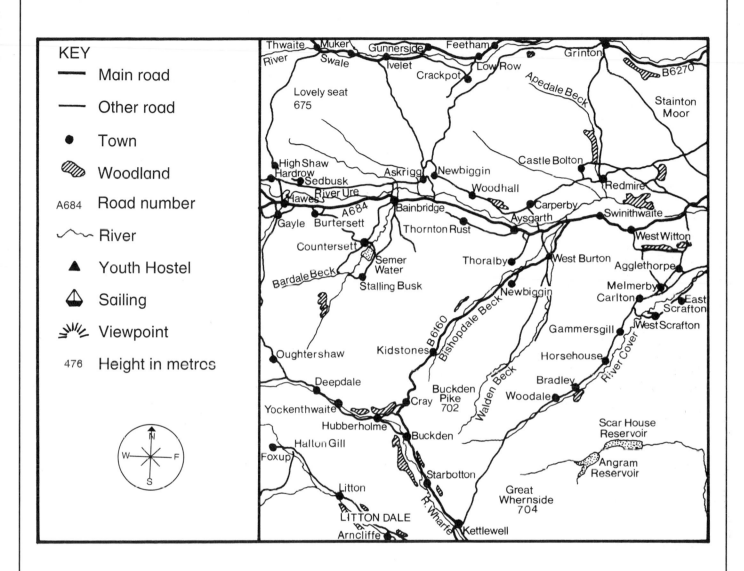

KEY

— Main road

— Other road

• Town

▨ Woodland

A684 Road number

〜 River

▲ Youth Hostel

⛵ Sailing

☀ Viewpoint

476 Height in metres

On the map:
1 Draw ▲ to show three places where you could stay.
2 Draw ⛵ to show where you could go sailing.
3 Draw ☀ to show the Buttertubs Pass.
4 Write 476 to show where the top of Addlebrough is.
5 Colour red the road from Bradley to Kettlewell.
6 Draw > on the road from Kettlewell to Bradley to show where it slopes downhill to Kettlewell.
7 Colour blue the road from Thwaite to Hawes.
8 Draw > on the road to show where it slopes downhill to Thwaite.
9 Draw hachures to show the shape of Great Whernside.
10 Draw > on the road from West Burton to Starbotton to show where it slopes downhill.

13 Looking at slopes

Name ....

Use photo **A** and map **B** on page 16 to help you.
This map shows the road between the hotel and Pen-y-graig.

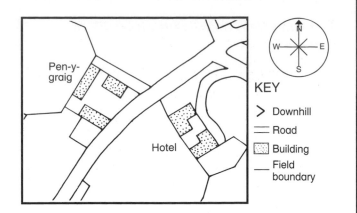

KEY

> Downhill
— Road
▦ Building
— Field boundary

1 On the road mark an arrow to show which way the road slopes downhill.
2 Which is on the higher land, Pen-y-graig or the hotel? Colour the buildings on the higher land brown.

These three maps show land which is sloping.
The arrows point downhill.
The cross-sections show the slopes of hills and valleys.
Only one cross-section goes with each map.

3 Colour the correct cross-section for each map.
4 Make some arrow maps and cross-sections of your own. Try them out on some of your friends.

Maps

Cross-sections

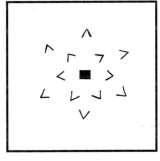

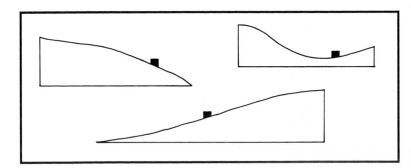

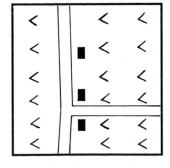

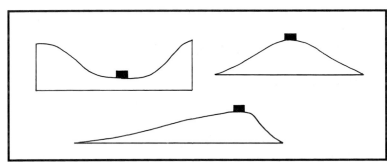

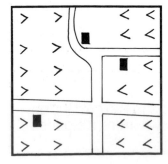

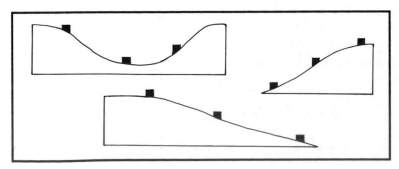

Page16 Landshape — showing height on maps

14 Higher and lower

Name ....

The map and the cross-section show part of the area on map **B** on page 16.
The cross-section shows how the land slopes downhill from east to west.

> ?
> 1 On the cross-section, write these words in the correct places:
> cliff
> flat
> gentle slope
> 2 On the map draw arrows to show where the land slopes downhill.

Map

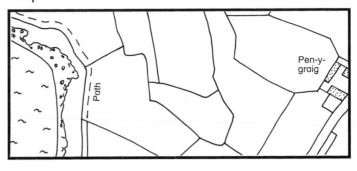

Cross-section

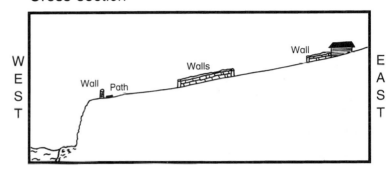

This is a map of an island.
It is a hilly island.
Use this information to show where the hills are and where the ground slopes.

> ?
> 3 Each stream starts in a hilly area.
> Draw hillocks to show the hills.
> 4 The land around the hut slopes down in all directions.
> Draw arrows to show the downhill slopes.
> 5 The northwest coast of the island has steep cliffs.
> Draw symbols to show the land is very rocky and steep.
> 6 Draw arrows on each river to show the way they flow downhill.
> 7 Use hillocks to show the land in the southwest of the island is hilly.

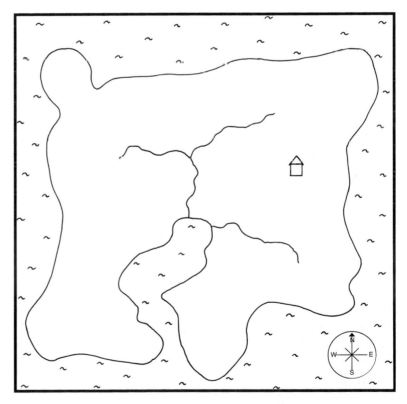

KEY

∧∧ Hilly   ꙮ Rocky outcrop   ~~ Sea

> Downhill slope   ~ River   ⌂ Hut

Page 16 Landshape — showing height on maps

15 Spot heights and contours

Name ....

In the box on the right you can see many spot heights.
They are numbered in metres (m).
Some are 10m. Some are 20m and 40m.
All the 30m spot heights have been joined by a line.

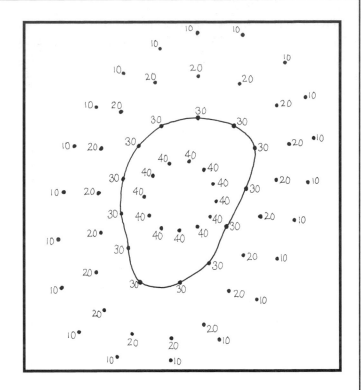

1 Join the 10m spot heights to each other by a line.
2 Join the 20m spot heights with a line.
3 Join the 40m spot heights with a line.

You have made a contour map of a hill.

4 What shape is it? _ _ _ _ _ _ _

In the box on the right are many spot heights.
You can see a stream, a road and buildings.
Find the sets of 20m, 40m, 60m, 100m and 120m spot heights.

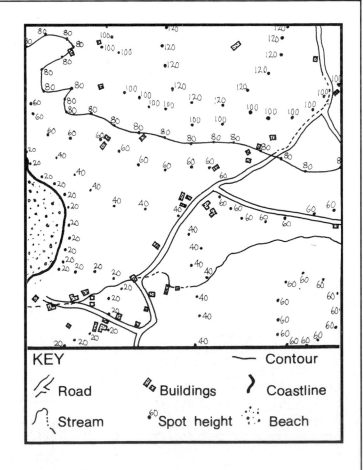

5 Join the 20m spot heights to each other with a line.
6 Now do the same for each of the other sets of spot heights.
   The 80m contour line has been drawn for you.

You have made a contour map.

7 Colour the beach orange.
8 Colour yellow all the land inside the highest contour line.
9 Colour green the land below the 20m contour line.
10 On the roads draw arrows to show where they go downhill.
11 Draw arrows on the stream to show where it flows downhill.
12 This map shows most of map **C** on page 17. Use map **C** to help you name the hotel, Swtan and Pen-y-foel on the map.

KEY

 ⟋⟋ Road   ◩ Buildings   ❯ Coastline
 ⟋⟍ Stream   60 Spot height   ∴ Beach
 — Contour

16 Contours

Here are three pictures.
Look carefully at them to see the shape of the land.

1 Look at each row of contour patterns.
Which pattern in each row goes with the picture?
Colour the correct one green.

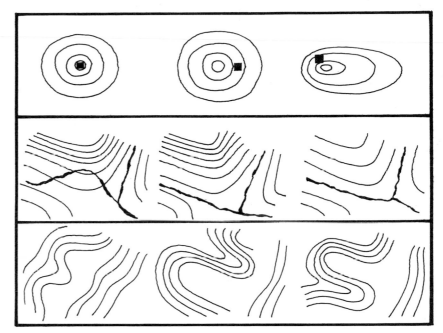

Here are three contour maps.
Look carefully at the shape and slope of the land.

2 Look at each row of pictures.
Colour the correct picture for each map.

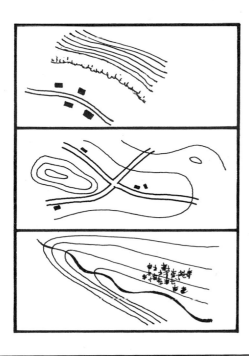

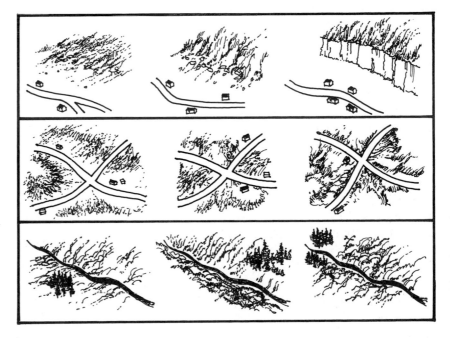

17 Contours and slopes

Name ....

This is a copy of map **C** on page 17.
It shows the contour lines and the roads.
Some of the contour lines are numbered to
show how high the land is.

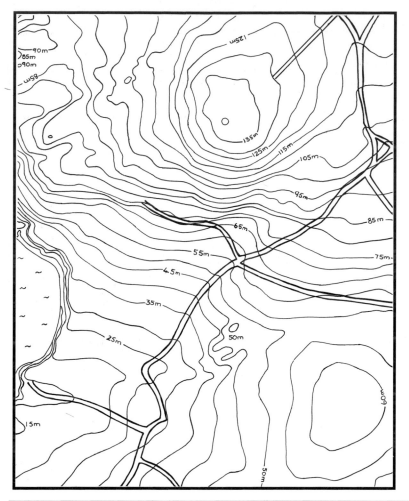

KEY

—75— Contours are at 5m vertical interval	☐ Land below 30 metres	～～ Sea
> Downhill slope	☐ Land above 100 metres	═══ Road

1 On each road mark arrows to show
  the way the land slopes
  downhill.
2 Colour light green land that is below the
  30m contour line.

3 Colour light brown land that
  is above the 100m contour
  line.
4 Draw an X to show where the tops of
  two hills are.

18 Six-figure grid references

1 Mark these grid references on the grid:
447,135; 495,135; 495,105; 447,105;
447,110; 445,109; 433,109; 432,111;
432,129; 433,131; 445,131; 447,131.

2 To find the shape they show join them together with a line.

3 Colour the shape.
What have you drawn? _ _ _ _ _ _ _

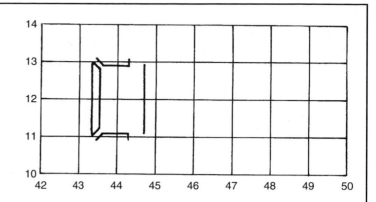

4 Mark these grid references on the grid and join them up:
261,545 to 247,545 to 247,576 to 304,576 to 304,524 to 261,524 to 261,545.

5 Mark and join together each pair of grid references:
261,545 to 269,545; 275,576 to 275,545;
281,545 to 304,545; 283,539 to 283,524;
277,537 to 277,524; 261,537 to 271,537.

6 Name each room on the plan you have drawn.

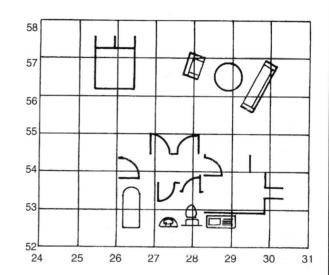

7 On the grid draw this map:
The road from the southwest ends at 214,622. A path runs from it northeast for 30m, then turns northwest for 20m, passing a well at 223,657. A canal flows straight across the area from 200,690 to 280,650. Between the road and the canal, to northwest and southeast is thick woodland. The path from the well crosses the canal at 248,666. On the northeast side of the canal is a house at 272,674. 5m south of it is a shed. The path stops there, having come via the west side of the house.

0   10   20   30   40   50m

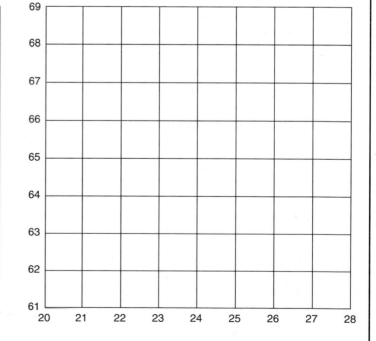

Page 18-19 Decreasing scales — a local area

19 The map puzzle

Name ....

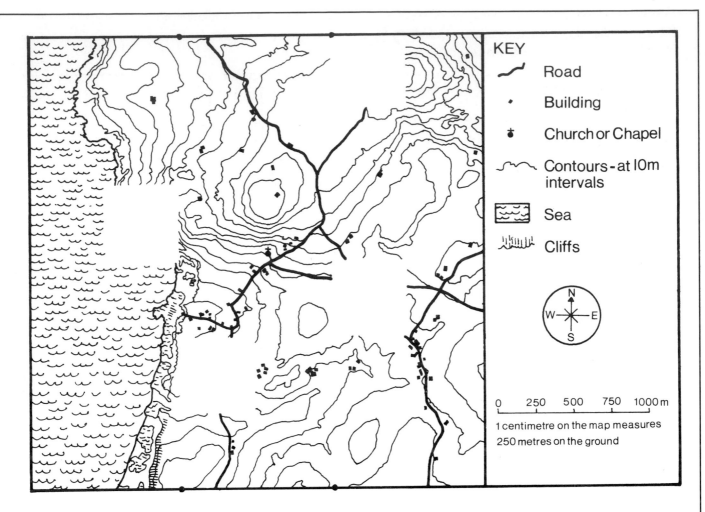

KEY

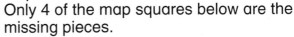

Look at the map.
Some parts of it have been left blank.
Its grid has not been finished.

Complete the grid.

1 Join the dots from top to bottom.
2 The western grid line is 29.
   Number each grid line along the bottom.
3 Mark dots at 4cm intervals up the side
   of the map.
   Join the dots from left to right.
4 The southern grid number is 88.
   Number each grid line up the left side.

Fit the missing pieces onto the map.
Only 4 of the map squares below are the
missing pieces.

5 Cut out the squares and work out which
   ones fit into the spaces.
   Stick the correct pieces onto the map.

Page 18-19 Decreasing scales — a local area

20 Shapes and patterns on maps 1

Name ....

You will need to use map **C** on page 19 to help you.

These three grid squares show part of map **C**.
1 Name the bay on the map.
2 Draw bridges to show where the roads cross a stream.

3 Four symbols are not shown in the key.
Draw them in the key.
Put them in the correct places on the map.

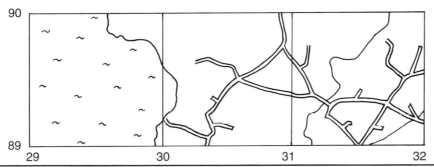

KEY

——— Road   Parking

~ Stream   Church

[~ ~] Sea   Public house

⊔ Bridge   Public telephone

This map is unfinished.
It shows only parts of the coastline of Anglesey in map **C**.

4 Draw in the parts of the coastline that are missing.

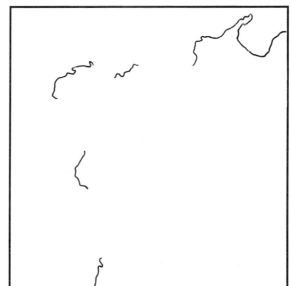

Find the area of woodland in the northwest of Anglesey.

5 Colour the shape in the box which shows its shape on the map.

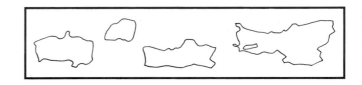

Look at these grid squares.
They show road patterns on map **C**.

6 Below each grid square write its grid reference.
7 Draw or colour one other feature in each grid square.

— — , — —   — — , — —   — — , — —

21 Shapes and patterns on maps 2

Name ....

You will need to use map **A** on page 20.

Two bridges cross the Menai Strait.
1 Draw them in the correct places on the map.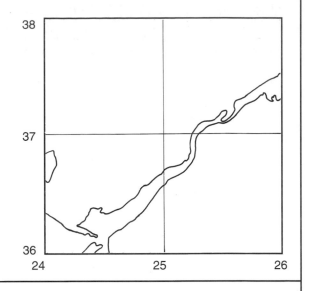

This map shows the pattern of the main roads on Anglesey.

2 On the map mark and name these towns:
    Holyhead
    Menai Bridge
    Benllech
    Amlwch
    Llangefni
3 Mark 6 campsites which are along the main roads.

KEY
═══ Main road
• Town
⚑ Camping

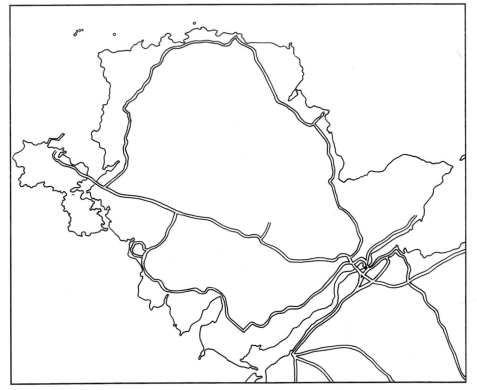

This map shows a grid square on map **A**. None of the places are named.

4 Write the grid numbers below and beside the map.
5 Name 5 villages on the map.
6 Mark 5 places where you can park a caravan.
7 Colour the beach yellow.

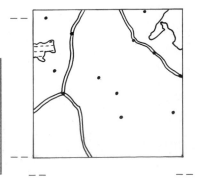

KEY
• Village
═══ Road
⊡ Reservoir
🚐 Caravan site

Pages 20-21 Decreasing scales - towns and regions

22 Shapes and patterns on maps 3

Name ....

Use map **B** on page 21 to help you.

1 Colour the map that shows the main road pattern you can see on map **B**.

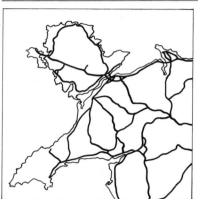
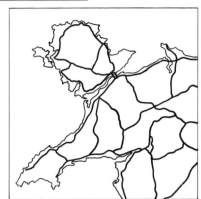
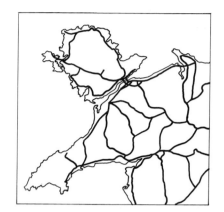

These grid squares have been enlarged from map **B**.
The scenic areas are shaded on each map.

2 Work out which grid squares they are.
Write the grid reference for each square.
3 On two squares colour the sea blue.

KEY

[dotted] Scenic area

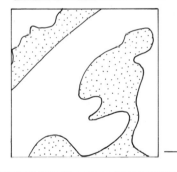
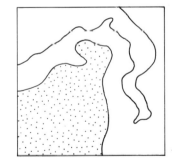
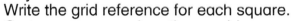
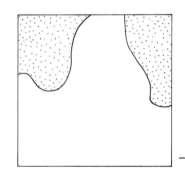

One of these maps shows the pattern of towns and villages on map **B**.

4 On the correct map colour the sea blue and the land green.
5 Name three towns or villages on the map.

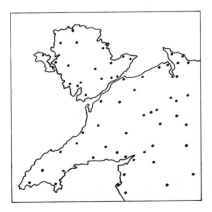
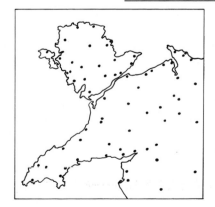
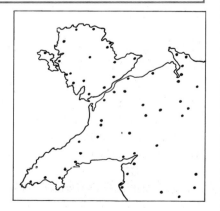

Page 20-21 Decreasing scales - towns and regions

23 Views of the globe

When you look at a globe you can only see half of it at one time.
The other half is hidden from view.

These two halves are called hemispheres, meaning half a sphere.
The globe is a sphere.

Here are two hemispheres.
1 On each, colour the land green and the sea blue. Complete the key.
2 Name the continents and oceans that you can see on each one.
3 Use an atlas to help you name five of the islands you can see on the two hemispheres.

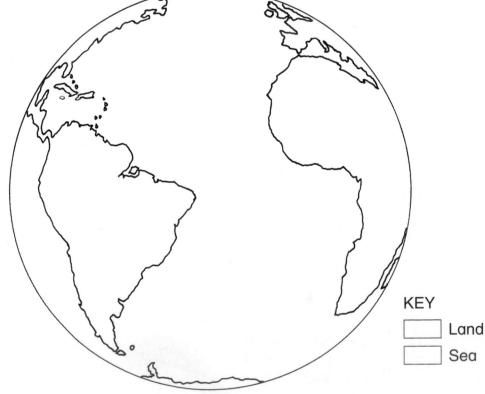

KEY

☐ Land
☐ Sea

Page 22-23 The shape of the Earth

24 From globe to map

These hemisphere maps
show the continents and
oceans.
You can also see them on
the world map.

1 Name each
   continent on the
   hemisphere maps and
   on the world map.
2 Draw lines to join each
   hemisphere map to the
   part of the world map it
   shows.

Pages 22-23 The shape of the Earth

© Collins-Longman Atlases 1993 Mapstart 3 Copymasters

25 Latitude and longitude 1

This is a copy of **A** on page 24.
The lines of latitude are marked but only some have been numbered.
They should be numbered every 20°.

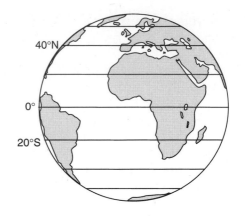

1 Write in the missing numbers of the lines of latitude.
   Write the letter N or S after each number.
2 Name the line of latitude numbered 0°:
   E_____

This is a copy of **B** on page 24.
The lines of longitude are marked but only some are numbered.
They should be numbered every 20°.

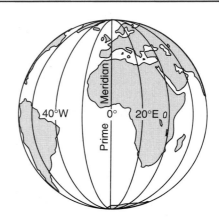

3 Write the missing numbers of the lines of longitude.
   Write the letter W or E after each number.
4 What is the number of the Prime Meridian? _

This is a copy of map **D** on page 24.

5 Complete the missing numbers for the lines of latitude and longitude.

6 Write the correct letter after each number.

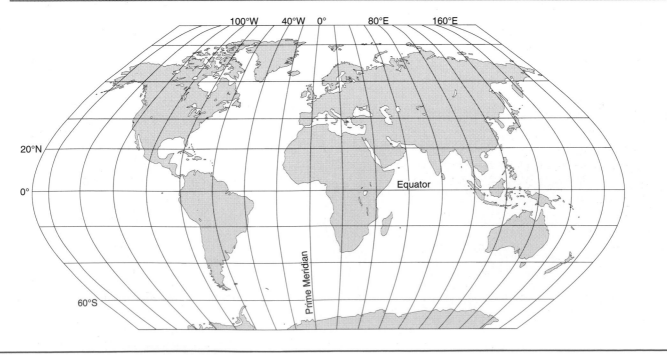

Pages 24-25 Where on Earth are we? Latitude and Longitude

26 Latitude and longitude 2

Name ....

This is a copy of map **E** on page 25.

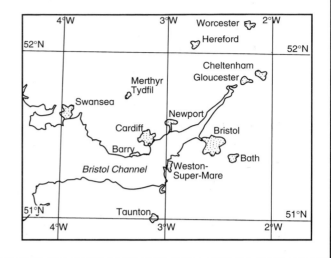

Find these towns from the grid references and first letters.
1 51N 2W: N.............................
2 51N 3W: C.............................
3 52N 2W: H.............................
4 51N 2W: G.............................
5 51N 3W: B.............................

This map shows Northern Ireland. Some of the towns have been named.
Use the grid references to name the other towns on the map.

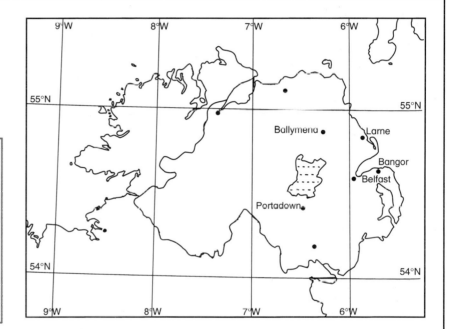

6 Name Sligo in grid square 54N 8W.
7 Name Londonderry in grid square 54N 7W.
8 Name Newry in grid square 54N 6W.
9 Name Coleraine in grid square 55N 6W.
10 Write Lough Neagh on the lake in 54N 6W.

Use the world map on pages 44-45 to help you.

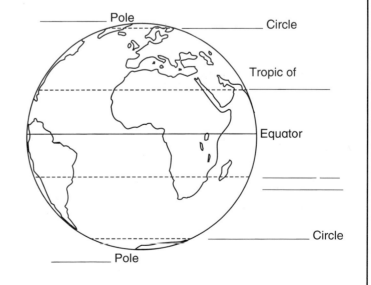

11 Write the names shown in the box below in the right places beside the globe.
12 Colour the land north of the equator brown and the land south of the equator green.

South Pole	Tropic of Capricorn
Antarctic Circle	North Pole
Tropic of Cancer	Arctic Circle

Pages 24-25 Where on Earth are we? Latitude and longitude

27 Latitude and longitude 3

Name ....

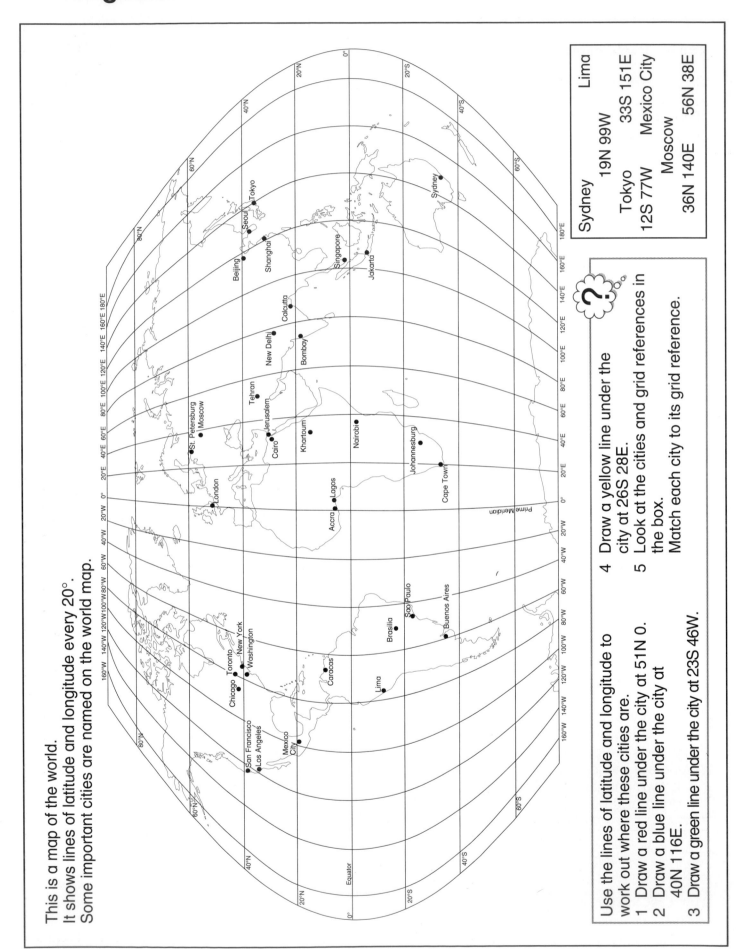

This is a map of the world.
It shows lines of latitude and longitude every 20°.
Some important cities are named on the world map.

Sydney	19N 99W	Lima	33S 151E
Tokyo	12S 77W	Mexico City	56N 38E
		Moscow	
36N 140E			

Use the lines of latitude and longitude to work out where these cities are.

1 Draw a red line under the city at 51N 0.
2 Draw a blue line under the city at 40N 116E.
3 Draw a green line under the city at 23S 46W.
4 Draw a yellow line under the city at 26S 28E.
5 Look at the cities and grid references in the box.
   Match each city to its grid reference.

Pages 24-25 Where on Earth are we? Latitude and longitude

28 What does the map show?

Name ....

You will need to use page 26.

This map shows campsites on an island in the United Kingdom.
Around the map there is no information to tell you what it is.
Other important information is missing too.

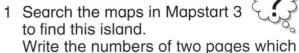

1 Search the maps in Mapstart 3 to find this island.
Write the numbers of two pages which will help you: _____ and _____
2 Work out what information is missing from around the map.
Write or draw it in.
3 Colour the map so that you can see what it shows clearly.

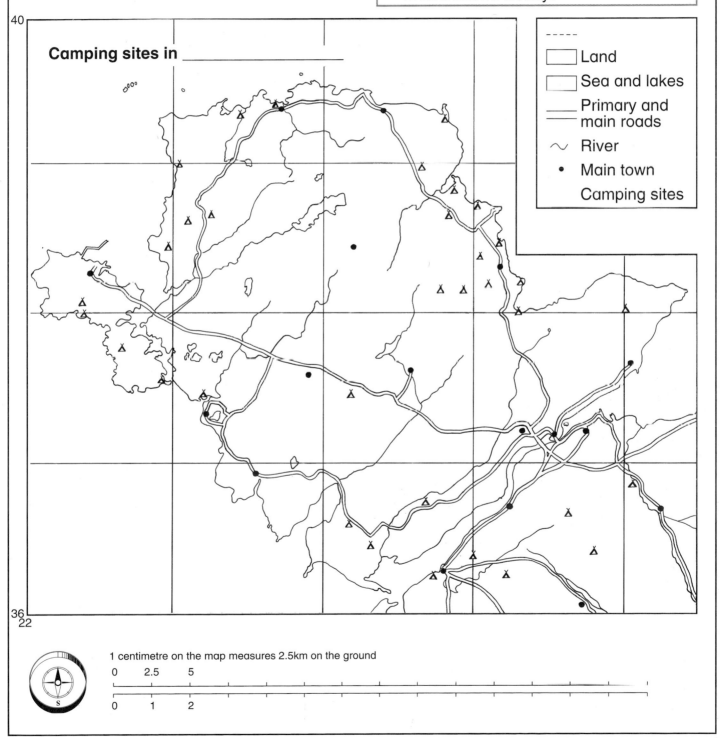

Camping sites in _____

Land
Sea and lakes
Primary and main roads
~ River
• Main town
Camping sites

1 centimetre on the map measures 2.5km on the ground

0   2.5   5

0   1   2

Pages 26-27 Introducing atlas maps

29 Shapes and patterns in Britain 1

Name ....

You will need to use the maps on pages 28 and 29.

This map shows a grid square from the map of Scotland.

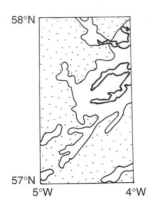

1 Which pattern does it show?_____

2 Colour the pattern the colour used on the map.

Look at the map on the right.
It shows a grid square from the map of Northern Ireland.

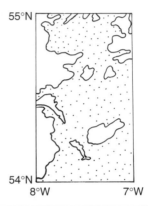

3 What pattern does it show?
_____

4 Colour the pattern the colour used on the map.

This map shows the pattern of one of the features you can see on the map of Scotland and Northern Ireland.

5 Name the pattern it shows:
_____

6 Colour the pattern the colour used on the map.

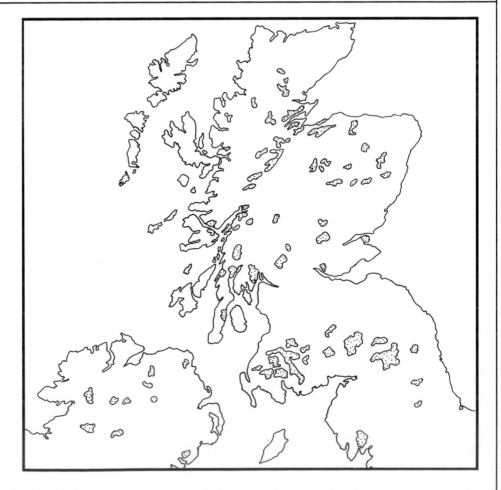

Pages 28-29 United Kingdom - Scotland and Northern Ireland

Name ....

You will need to use the map on pages 30 and 31.

These maps show the towns in two grid squares on map **A** of England and Wales.

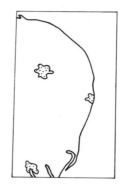
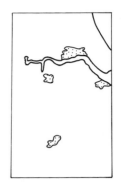

1 Write the latitude and longitude of each grid square.
2 Name one town in each grid square.

Find these three grid squares on map **A**. They show the pattern of one type of landuse.

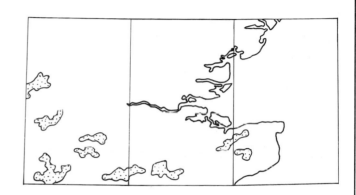

3 Write the latitude and longitude for the grid squares.
4 Colour the landuse pattern the same colour as the map.

Look at these maps of parts of the United Kingdom.

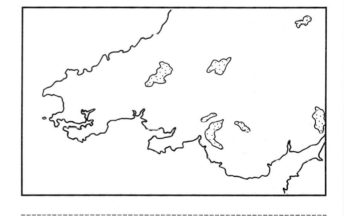

5 Which area of the United Kingdom does each map show? Write the area below each map.
6 One of the maps shows the pattern of moorland.
   Colour the correct pattern light green.
7 What patterns do the other maps show?

_____   _____

-----------------------------   ------

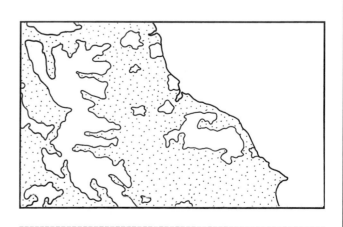

----

31 Holiday journeys

Four families go on holiday from Dover. They each like to drive on the motorway as far as they can, but they also like to go by the shortest route on main roads.
On the map show the routes they might choose for their journeys.

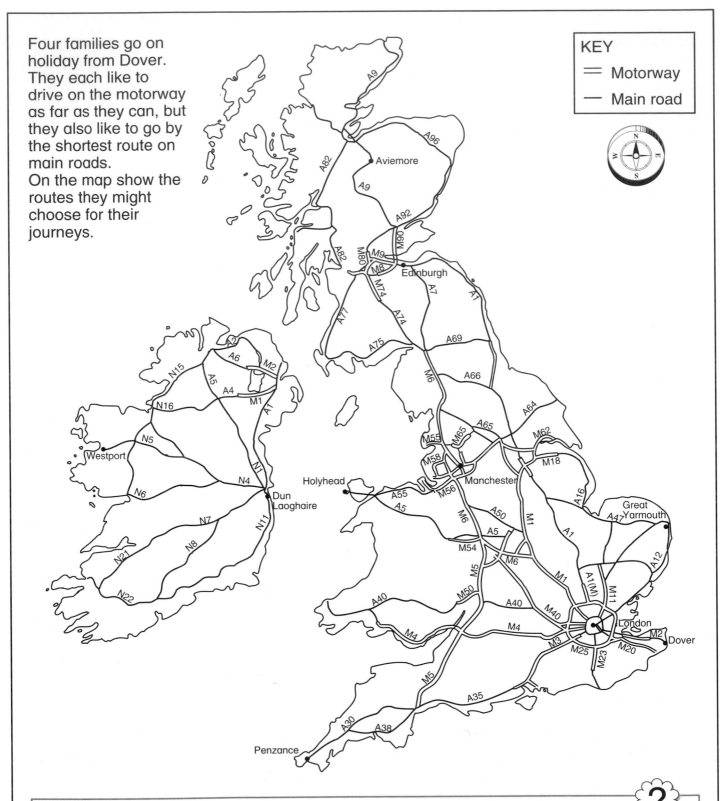

KEY
= Motorway
— Main road

1 In brown, draw the Lee's route to Great Yarmouth.
   They visit London on the way.
2 In blue, draw the Rahman's route to Penzance.
3 In green, draw the O'Connor's route to

Westport. They go from Holyhead to Dun Laoghaire by ferry.
4 In red draw the Mackay's route to Aviemore.
   They stay overnight in Manchester and Edinburgh on the way.

32 Looking at thematic maps

Name ....

You will need to use the maps on pages 32 to 35.

Look at these two maps.
Each shows an extract from the recreation and population maps of the British Isles.

1 Which area of the British Isles and which theme does each map show?
Write the area and theme below each map.

2 Colour each map.

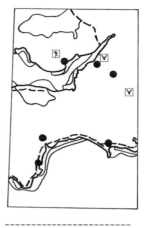

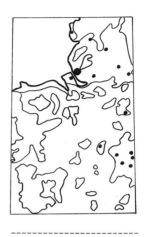

These maps show two areas in the United Kingdom.
For each area one map shows recreation and one map shows population.

3 Name one National Park in the top left map:

_____

4 Name the city in the bottom right map:

_____

5 Above the maps write which are the recreation maps and which are the population maps.

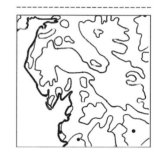

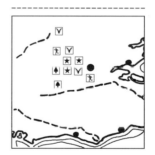

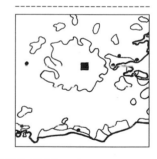

This map shows Exmoor in map **C** on page 33.
The squares on the map show the pattern of one of the recreation uses on map **C**.

6 Name the pattern which the map shows.

_____

_____

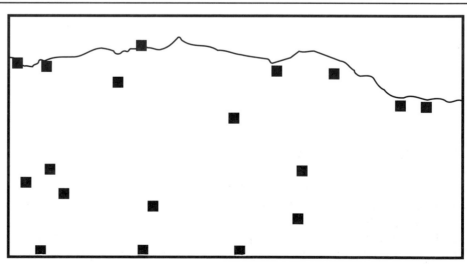

Pages 32-35 British Isles – Recreation and Population

33 Map the weather

This is today's weather forecast.

"**London, SE, Central S England, Midlands, N and S Wales, Isle of Man, N Ireland**: dry with sunny periods; wind SE light; max temp -1° to 1°C (30° to 34°F).
E Anglia, E, NW, Central N, NE England: dry with sunny periods; wind SE moderate; max temp -4° to 0°C (24° to 32°F).
Channel Islands, SW England: cloudy with occasional sleet showers in places; wind SE strong; max temp 0° to 3°C (32° to 38°F).
Lake District, Borders, Edinburgh, Dundee: rather cloudy with isolated occasional snow showers; wind SE light; max temp -1° to 1°C (30° to 34°F).
SW Scotland, Glasgow, Central Highlands, NW Scotland: dry with sunny periods; wind SE light; max temp -1° to 1°C (30° to 34°F).
Aberdeen, NE Scotland, Orkney, Shetland: cloudy with snow showers; wind SE moderate; max temp 0° to 2°C (32° to 36°F)."

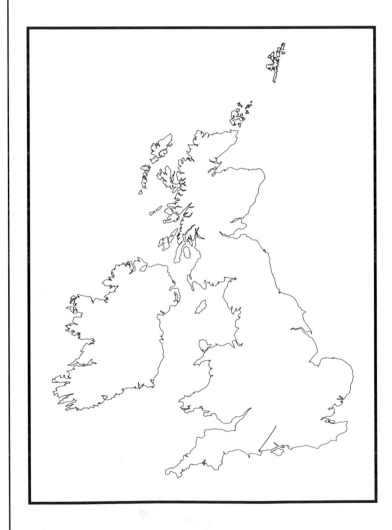

KEY

☐	Sunshine
☐	Cloudy with sunny spells
☐	Sleet showers
☐	Snow showers
☐	Highest temperature (°C)
☐	Wind direction

1 In the key to the weather map, draw symbols for each element of the weather.

2 Use your symbols to map the weather forecast onto the British Isles map.

34 The British Isles

Name ....

This is a map of the British Isles.
Use the map on page 39 to help you.

Use the map on page 39 to help you.

1 Join up the latitude and
   longitude grid lines.
   Number them correctly.
2 Name the features marked on the map.

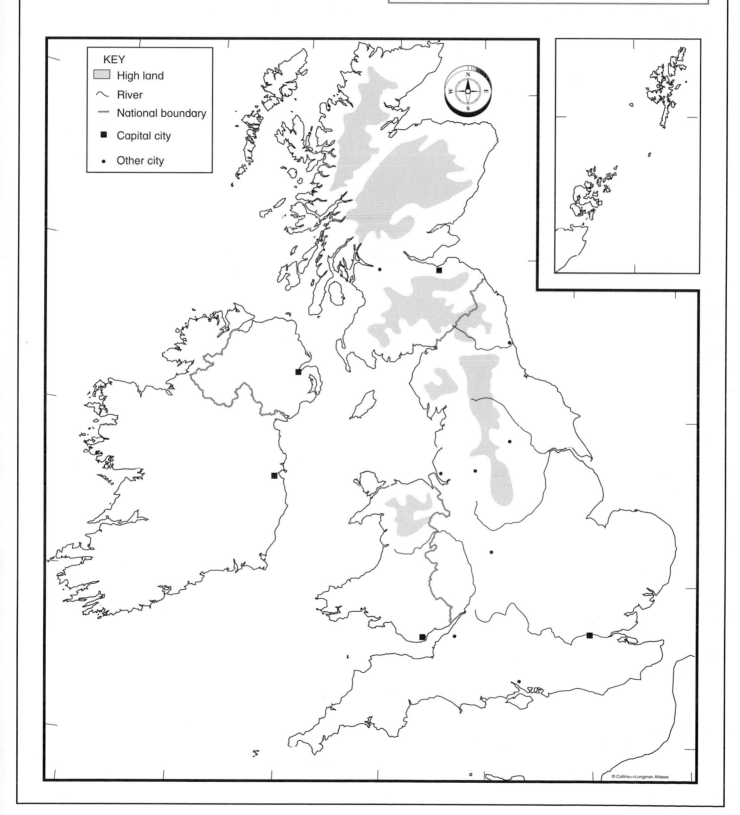

KEY
☐ High land
∿ River
⠿ National boundary
■ Capital city
• Other city

© Collins<>Longman Atlases

Name ....

This is a map of Europe.
Use the satellite photo and map on pages
40 and 41 to help you.

PORTUGAL	LUXEMBOURG	DENMARK
FRANCE	GREECE	ITALY	SPAIN
BELGIUM	NETHERLANDS	GERMANY

1 On the map name the countries in the box and mark their capital cities.
2 Mark and name on the map the mountains called the Alps.
3 Complete the key.

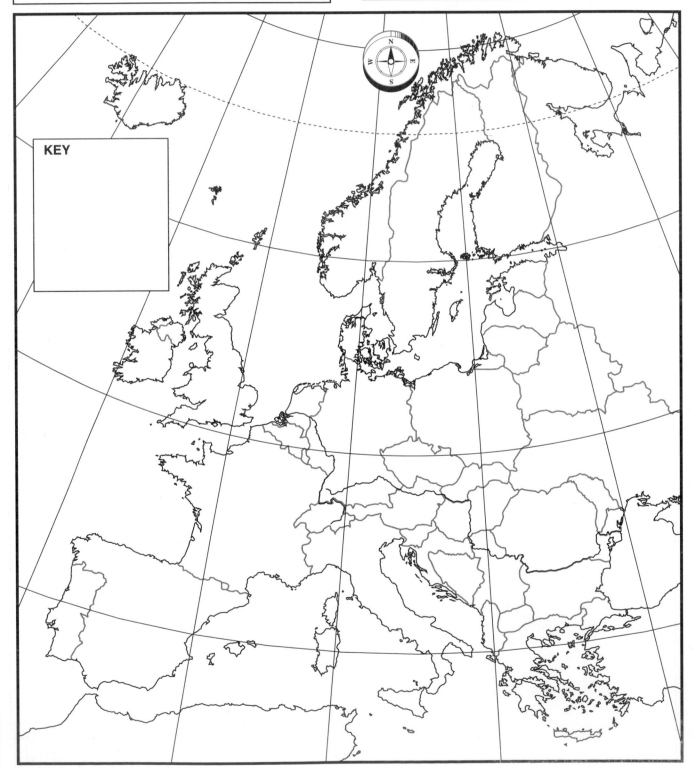

KEY

36 Shapes and patterns in Europe

Name ....

You will need to use the photo and map on pages 40 and 41.

Look at the shapes in the box.
They show five countries.

1 Find the countries on map **B**.
Write the name next to each country.

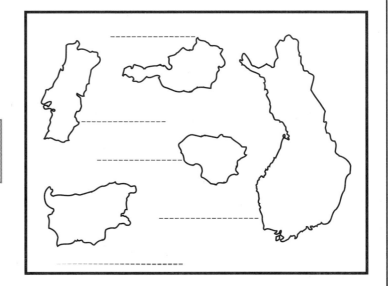

These shapes show islands and lakes in Europe.

2 Work out which are the islands and which are the lakes. Colour the islands green and the lakes blue.
3 Write the name next to each island and lake.

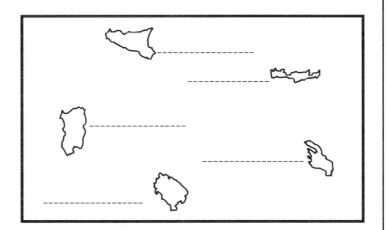

This map of Europe shows some of the main mountain areas.
The names are above and below the map.

4 Use an atlas to find out where the mountains are. Join each name to its mountain area on the map.

PYRENEES   CARPATHIAN MTS.   ALPS

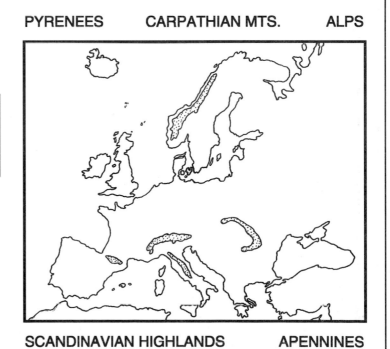

SCANDINAVIAN HIGHLANDS   APENNINES

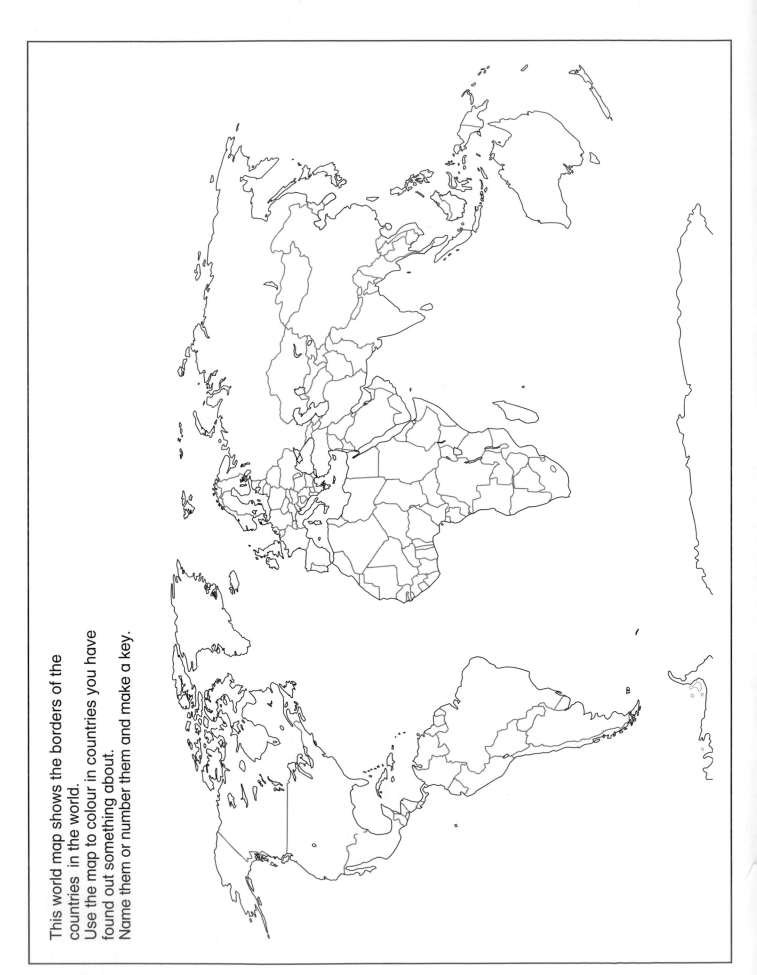

This world map shows the borders of the countries in the world.
Use the map to colour in countries you have found out something about.
Name them or number them and make a key.